acknowledgements

My thanks to Denis Kitchen, Dave Schreiner, Ray Fehrenbach and the KSP production staff, Steve Stiles, William Stout for the splendid introduction, Joseph Schultz and, of course, Denise.

—Mark Schultz

credits

Mark Schultz *creator, writer, artist*
Steve Stiles *artist, additional stories*
Denise Prowell *lettering, cover color*
Denis Kitchen *publisher*
Dave Schreiner *editor*
Ray Fehrenbach *art director*
Kevin Lison *design*
Michael Eastman,
Tamara Sibert,
Kristen Hylton *production*
Jamie Riehle *marketing*
William Stout *introduction*
Jim Kitchen *v-p, operations*

Library of Congress Cataloging-in-Publication Data

Schultz, Mark, 1955–
    [Xenozoic tales. Issues 9-12]
    Time in overdrive / by Mark Schultz
        p.   cm.
    Originally published: 1989-1992.
    ISBN 0-87816-213-5 (signed and numbered hardcover, $29.95) --
    ISBN 0-87816-214-3 : $14.95 (pbk.)
    I. Title.
PN6728.X46S3925   1993
741.5'973-dc20   93-23952
                                                          CIP

Time in Overdrive is published by Kitchen Sink Press, Inc., 320 Riverside Dr., Northampton, MA, 01060. Contents copyright © 1989, 1990, 1991, 1992, 1993 by Mark Schultz. All rights reserved. Introduction copyright © 1993 by William Stout. Compilation copyright © 1993 by Kitchen Sink Press, Inc. "Cadillacs and Dinosaurs" is a trademark of General Motors Corporation used under license by Kitchen Sink Press, Inc. **Time in Overdrive** collects the comic book **Xenozoic Tales**, issues 9-12. Issues 1-4 were reprinted in *Cadillacs and Dinosaurs*™; issues 5-8 were reprinted in *Dinosaur Shaman*. Printed in Canada. Printing number 10 9 8 7 6 5 4 3 2

table of contents

4 | Introduction
by William Stout

6 | Sketchbook
by Mark Schultz
pencil and ink character and concept sketches

17 | Last Link in the Chain
written and drawn by Mark Schultz
from Xenozoic Tales #9

37 | The Aqueduct
written by Mark Schultz
art by Steve Stiles
from Xenozoic Tales #9

45 | Lords of the Earth
written and drawn by Mark Schultz
from Xenozoic Tales #10

65 | Fields of Expertise
written by Mark Schultz
art by Steve Stiles
from Xenozoic Tales #10

73 | A Woman's Work...
written by Mark Schultz
art by Steve Stiles
from Xenozoic Tales #12

81 | Primeval
written and drawn by Mark Schultz
from Xenozoic Tales #11

101 | Report From the Resistance
written by Mark Schultz
art by Steve Stiles
from Xenozoic Tales #11

109 | Two Cities
written and drawn by Mark Schultz
from Xenozoic Tales #12

CLOSE ENCOUNTERS of the XENOZOIC KIND

by William Stout

I'll never forget the first time I encountered Mark Schultz's *Xenozoic Tales*. No, I can't claim to be so hip as to have read it from its first appearance in *Death Rattle* #8 (although upon discovering that there had been a previous Xenozoic tale, I immediately ferreted out that issue). It was *Xenozoic Tales* #1 that hit me like a cinder block and left me laughing like a fool.

My God, I was slap happy upon encountering this stuff for the first time! Here was a guy who was not just doing Wally Wood, but who was aping a particularly great *week* Wood had had in a particularly good *year*!

Who was this guy, Mark Schultz? With this magnificent and fully-realized art rushing into the public consciousness like a freight train from nowhere, I had to immediately reconsider the possibility of channeling. Schultz's output seemed rather rapid at first, considering the awesome care and quality that went into each book. And just as quickly Mark's art was transforming. He was like this colossal, unstoppable Art Sponge from the Abyss, absorbing comic art's greatest hits in brisk succession. WHAM! Frazetta! POW! Williamson! ZAP! Roy Krenkel! Yet after a short stylistic pregnancy during which all of these great influences were consumed and digested, the work ultimately reemerged as pure Mark Schultz. It was as though Mark had to compress and assimilate these artists' styles into his own work at breakneck speed so that he could get to himself as quickly as possible.

I continue to examine and savor the work. Here is a guy who is committed 100%. No line, not one detail, whether it be in the architecture, the furniture, the figure work, the dinosaurs or the cars is spared in this book. You won't find *even one panel* that was tossed off to save a little time. Total commitment. Period.

Now the guy I would hate to be is Steve Stiles. You could be the Second Coming of the illegitimate son of an unholy union between Johnny Craig and Jack Davis and *still* be compared unfavorably with Mark Schultz. Steve has got THE tough act to follow, and he does it with a rock solid dignity and integrity. And thank God, he doesn't try to be Mark Schultz.

I can't exactly remember the first time I met Mark. We didn't meet until after several issues of *Xenozoic Tales* had been published. I remember thinking about tracking this guy down and asking to do a guest cover, but I stopped myself, reasoning *it would mean one less Schultz cover.* I couldn't bear the thought of that. I know a first meeting with Mark Schultz should be burned forever into one's brain like the birth of one's first child, or the purchase of your first E.C. comic book, but in my case, it's not (they say that with age the memory is the first thing to go—I can't recall what the second thing is). I do recollect, just prior to meeting Mark, that Al Williamson called me and said, "You gotta meet Mark Schultz—he's one of the good guys; he's a sweetheart." Al is rarely (if ever) wrong about things like good and evil and I looked forward to meeting Mark with great anticipation. I knew just from the fact that we shared so many similar influences that there was a high likelihood that we'd have a lot in common.

It was probably at a San Diego Comicon. I *do* remember not having nearly as much time as I wanted with Mark (I'll bet there's a lot of his fans who feel this way), and that, sure enough, just as Al had told me, Mark was indeed "one of the good guys."

Besides being a Good Guy, what's Mark Schultz like? He is quiet and soft spoken, yet firm, strong and direct in his opinions. He is humble, yet knows the value of his work. And he is, above all, a gentleman of the first order.

We got other chances at other conventions to spend time together. Once Al conspired to have a grand meeting of the Good Lizard Men—a term Williamson coined to describe guys who are adept at drawing dinosaurs—and had the three of us invited to a wonderful convention in Toronto. One night our gracious host, John Biernat, invited us to his home to see his fabulous art and book collection. That was a real high point of our Toronto stay, for the three of us are connoisseurs and collectors almost as much as we are artists. At one point, John pulled out a stack of Joseph Clement Coll dupes from his collection. Mark and I had our credentials as gentlemen tested to the limit when he offered the stack to us if we could devise a way to split them among ourselves. That we are still friends to this day I believe speaks volumes about our restraint in that delicate situation.

Oddly enough, I never saw an original *Xenozoic* page until about two years ago. Mark and I were both guests at a convention in Texas. After surviving the assault of someone known locally as "Corn Boy," I hobbled over to Mark's table. He pulled out some pages he had completed recently. I tried to maintain my equanimity while my brain did a Tex Avery take. This was the finest inking I had seen since Frank Frazetta in his prime! Although Kitchen Sink Press has held to high standards in the production of *Xenozoic Tales*, the printed version of this work bears absolutely no comparison to the original pages. If you ever get the chance to view some of Mark's original work, jump on it.

I have to confess to a little dark and dirty secret—Mark doesn't even know this: I never actually *read Xenozoic Tales* until fairly recently (though obviously I'm a bit nuts for the art; right now I'm trying to get a hold of the different *Xenozoic* candy wrappers). I think perhaps I feared that the quality of the stories would not live up to the standards set by the exquisite art. My advice now is to have more trust and faith in your friends. The writing is as densely textured and polished as the art. Imperfect heroes, political intrigues and veiled contemporary sociopolitical overtones all work to make this one of the most compelling tales in the world of comics. Schultz's examination of contemporary ecopolitics through the crises that affect his Xenozoic world make *Xenozoic Tales* a riveting blend of the old and the new. It's *Prisoner of Zenda* meets the Reagan cabinet. There is plenty of action—but there are quiet moments, too. It's the execution of those quiet moments in comics that separates the men from the boys; and sorry, boys—but Mark's got it in spades there as well. Because of the complex layers in Mark's storytelling, *Xenozoic Tales* has less the feel of a comic book series and more the impression and weight of a *Prince Valiant*-style epic. Ultimately, *Xenozoic Tales* is a richly drawn saga of heroic, novel-like proportions.

You hold in your hands the work of a true Art God, someone who loves what he does and someone who *truly cares* that you love what he does. So sink into your favorite chair and slowly turn the page that will usher you forward in time into the lost and now found Xenozoic Era in all its splendor, all its savageness, and in all its glory. Before you are the black and white threads of a tapestry that all of us *Xenozoic Tales* fans hope Mark Schultz will continue to weave forever.

Qua Hoon!

(In his artistic career, William Stout has worked comfortably in comics, films, and in the field of fine art. One of his more recent efforts in the latter was the still-traveling exhibition of 45 paintings, Dinosaurs, Penguins and Whales—the Wildlife of Antarctica. *He is currently working on the book,* Lost World: Modern and Prehistoric Life in Antarctica, *which will contain sketches and paintings done while spending two months there in late 1992.*)

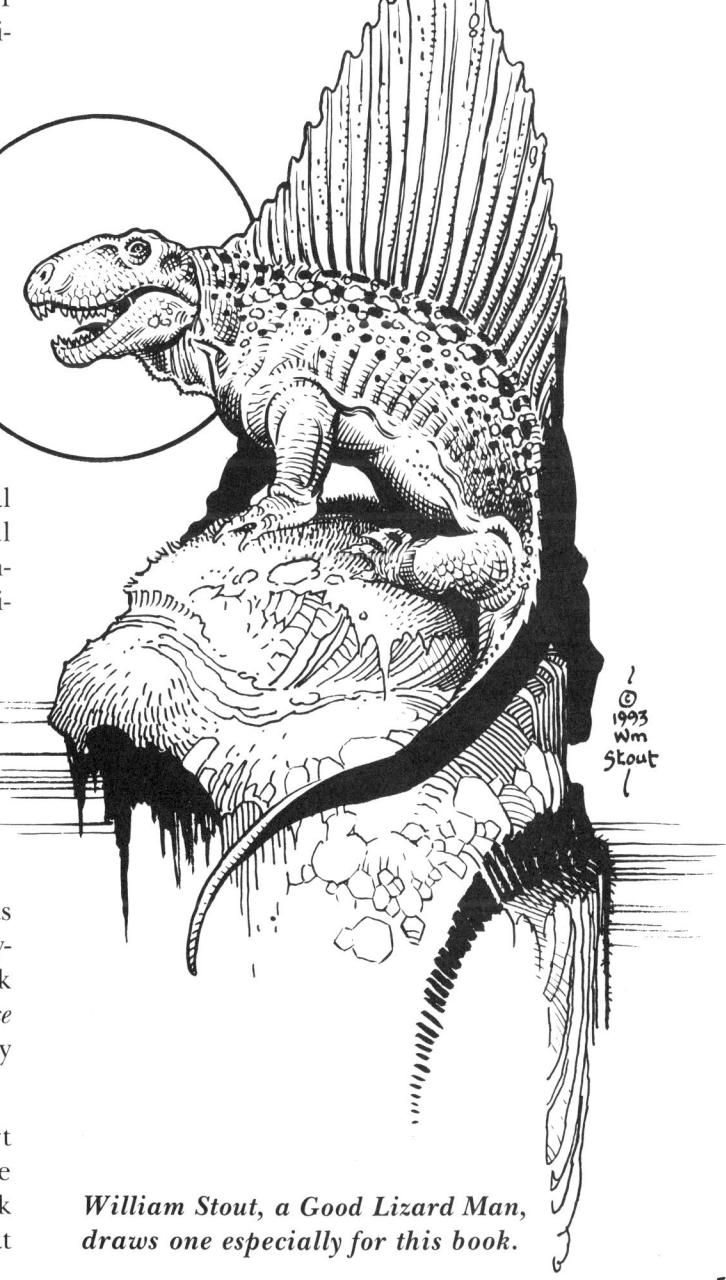

William Stout, a Good Lizard Man, draws one especially for this book.

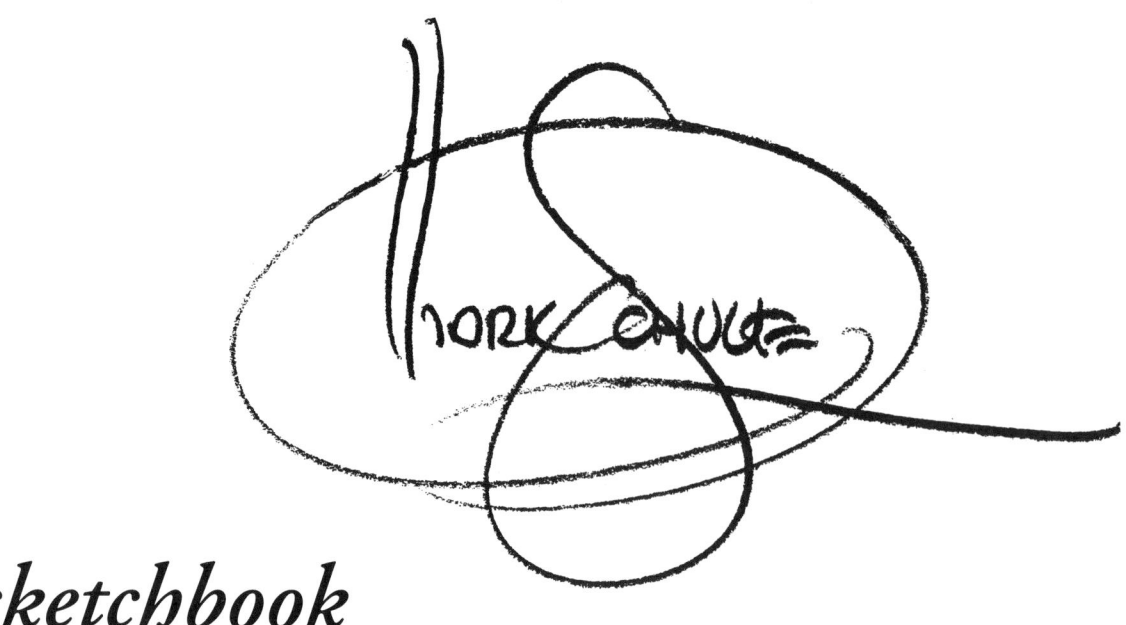

sketchbook

On the following pages, we present sketches by the Best Artist (Harvey Awards) in comic books three out of four consecutive years. The Harveys are awarded by a professional vote. The sketches here cover Mark's work for comic books, a portfolio and serigraph, general drawings and for the *Cadillacs and Dinosaurs*™ television show.

Preliminary sketch for the cover of *Time in Overdrive*.

Pencil rough for a plate in a Schultz portfolio coming in 1994.

Simplified sketches of Jack and Hannah, used as model sheets for the new *Cadillacs & Dinosaurs* Saturday morning T.V. show, coming in September, 1993, on CBS.

Opposite page–
Pencil sketch of Jack Tenrec.

Preliminary sketch for a Schultz serigraph, "Chance Meeting on the Veldt".

Pencil sketch of Tyrannosaurus tracking three Triceratops.

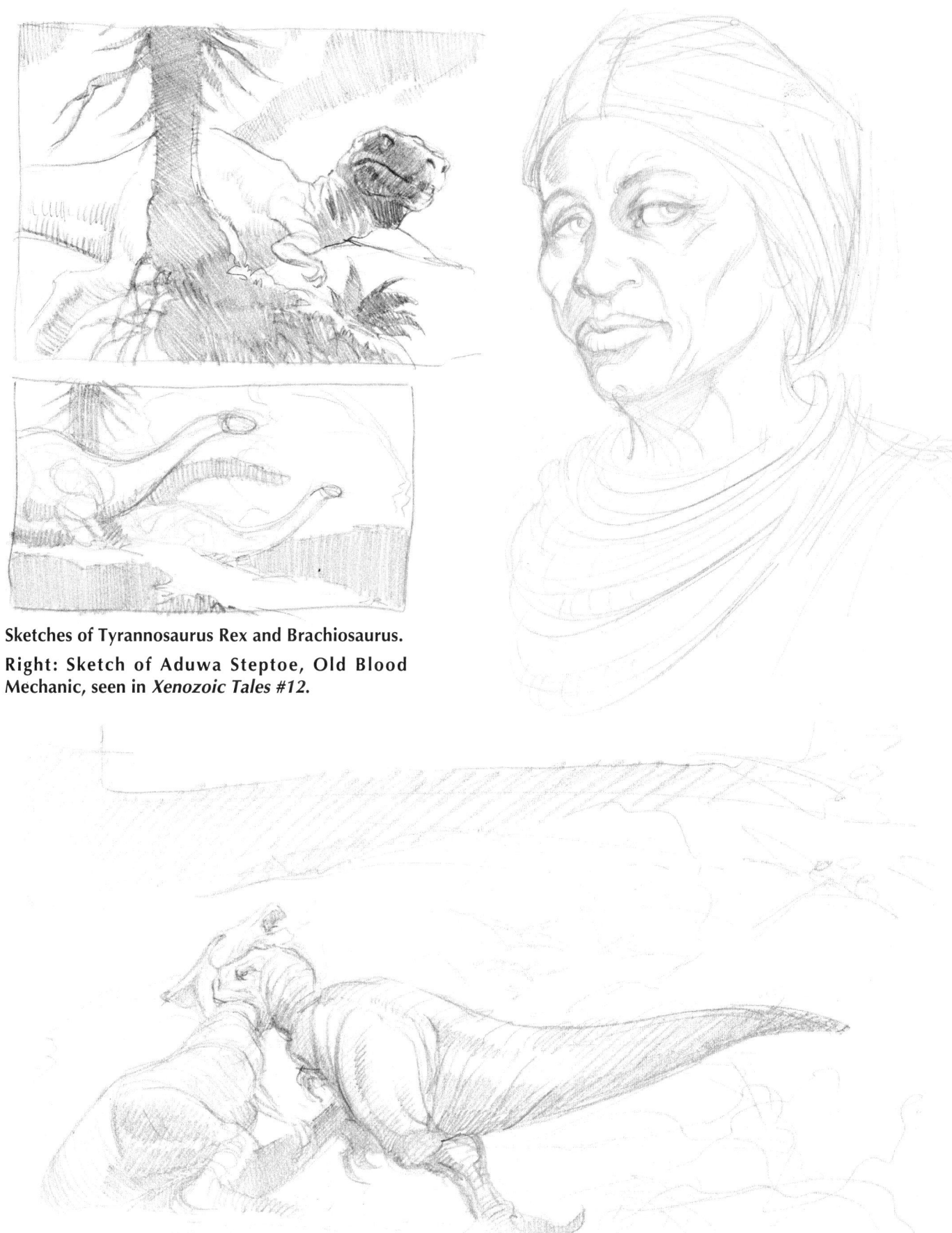

Sketches of Tyrannosaurus Rex and Brachiosaurus.

Right: Sketch of Aduwa Steptoe, Old Blood Mechanic, seen in *Xenozoic Tales #12*.

Dinosaurs in battle.

Character sketches for a new story, "On Dangerous Ground," in *Xenozoic Tales #13*. Balclutha, a new character, was inspired by Lyle Lovett.

HANNAH'S BALLROOM GOWN

Progression – Evolution of a splash page: "On Dangerous Ground," to be published in *Xenozoic Tales #13*, features a grand ball welcoming Hannah back to her city. In the four pieces here, Schultz designs and pencils the layout of the scene.

THE CREW STOOD AT THE GAPING MOUTH OF THE GREAT UNFINISHED WATER MAIN, THEIR WORK ON THE NEW AQUEDUCT TEMPORARILY SUSPENDED. JUST BEYOND TOWERED THE **OLD** AQUEDUCT, SO CLOSE THEY COULD ALMOST TOUCH IT, WAITING TO BE CONNECTED TO THE **NEW**.... WAITING TO BE RELIEVED OF ITS RESPONSIBILITIES AS THE CITY IN THE SEA'S SOURCE OF LIFE. EVERYTHING WAITED FOR THE MEN SENT DOWN THE PIPE....

THE AQUEDUCT

MUSTAPHA CAIRO SHIFTED HIS GAZE BACK AND FORTH BETWEEN THE OLD AND NEW STRUCTURES AND CRITICALLY STUDIED BOTH. SEVENTY-FIVE YEARS AGO HIS GRANDFATHER HAD BEGUN THE ELDER STRUCTURE. THIRTY-FIVE YEARS AGO HIS FATHER HAD COMPLETED IT, PROVIDING FOR THE FIRST TIME A DEPENDABLE FLOW OF FRESH WATER TO THE SEAGIRT CITY.

IT WAS ONLY FITTING THEN THAT THE COUNCIL HAD COME TO HIM TO HELP COMPLETE THE **REROUTING** OF THE WATER MAIN. OVER MANY LONG MONTHS HE HAD DESIGNED, ENGINEERED AND SUPERVISED THE DIFFICULT CONSTRUCTION OF THE NEW AQUEDUCT. NOW, WITH ONLY THE FINAL TASK OF JOINING HIS CONSTRUCT TO THE OLD MAIN REMAINING, HE HAD SENT THREE MEN DOWN THE PIPELINE INTO THE BOWELS OF THE CITY.

THAT WAS OVER THREE HOURS AGO....

AS THE SURVIVORS SCRAMBLED BACK OUT OF THE CHAMBER, MUSTAPHA SWUNG HIS LAMP AROUND FOR ONE LAST LOOK....

THE ATTACK CEASED ONCE THEY RETURNED TO THE PIPE....

HE WAS LEFT WITH THE IMPRESSION OF HUGE LOCKS.... MIGHTY WATER GATES....

Mustapha did not have to wait long....

Before he departed for the rendezvous, he called for a team of SPECIALISTS....

At a quarter till midnight he and Isambard disappeared into the night....

FIELDS OF EXPERTISE

THE MACHINATIO VITAE TEACHES US THAT THE MOST HONORABLE PATH A MAN CAN FOLLOW LEADS HIM DOWN INTO THE SOIL. WE WHO HAVE CHOSEN A LIFE OF FARMING HAVE ALWAYS CAREFULLY TRIED TO FOLLOW THE PRINCIPLES SET FORTH BY THE **DOCTRINE**, AS TAUGHT BY THE **OLD BLOOD MECHANICS**, JACK TENREC FOREMOST AMONG THEM.

THE DOCTRINE MAY SEEM **CRUEL** AT TIMES, BUT THE CALAMITIES VISITED UPON OUR ANCESTORS CLEARLY SHOW THE FOLLY IN ATTEMPTING TO SUBJUGATE THE LAND.

WE KNEW THE LIFE WASN'T GOING TO BE EASY. WE KNEW THAT BEFORE WE CAME. BUT SOME OF US JUST COULDN'T STAND BEING COOPED UP IN THE CITY, NOTHING BUT WATER ON ALL SIDES.

HOW MANY OF US GET THE CHANCE TO DO WHAT WE REALLY WANT? TO WORK WITH THE EARTH...

TO LEARN TO BEND AND ACCEPT ADVERSITY... THE NEVER ENDING CRUSH OF THE ENCROACHING JUNGLE...

THE TEMPERAMENTAL SOIL, QUICK TO REJECT OUR CROPS...

THE HORDES OF INSECTS, ATTRACTED BY OUR SUCCESSES...

AND THE SLITHERS, **RULERS OF THE INTERIOR**, BOLDLY RAIDING OUR STOCK...

DISDAINFUL OF OUR DEFENSES...

BROWSING WHEREVER THEIR WHIMS TAKE THEM.

"GIT OUTTA THERE! GIT! GIT!"

STILL, WHEN THE SLITHERS HAVE BEEN PERSUADED TO LEAVE, AND THEIR GUANO HAS BEEN RAKED INTO THE SOIL, THE CROPS GROW BACK BETTER THAN EVER.

AND THE PREDATORY BUGS SEEM TO TAKE CARE OF MOST OF THE PESTS.

EVERYTHING SEEMS TO PRETTY MUCH EVEN OUT... WHICH IS HOW THE DOCTRINE TEACHES US IT SHOULD BE...

BUT IT *IS* A HARSH LIFE.

ESPECIALLY THOSE SETBACKS THAT NEVER SEEM TO CARRY *ANY* ADVANTAGES...

RRRUUMMM BBBLLLEE

THE *QUAKES*...

THE *BLIGHTS*...

THE *DROUGHTS*...

Word also has it that she's using the ancients' super guns to massacre whole herds of wildlife.

Scharnhorst is loosing all the evil from which the Machinatio Vitae protected us.

But the tribe majority continue to see her as a savior, even as they gasp at her blasphemous policies.

I can't entirely blame them, either.

They see the City's larder filling for the first time. They see the swamps draining and they think it means an end to disease.

But they ignore what they know to be true. Someday the balance will come due.

The fools! Can't they feel the tension already?

I'm sure you've heard about the destruction of Scharnhorst's larder in the Tennaguru section...

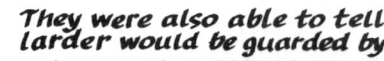

Herme's could never be called docile. In his present role he grows increasingly intractable. I know we'll have to release him soon...

Until then he serves us well.

Despite Scharnhorst's attempts to conceal the destruction of her larder, word has gotten out.

Fearful rumors are circulating through the tribe concerning the hideous, shambling marauder they imagine striking at will.

Still, I fear it will be a long campaign before the tribe turns from its new found "prosperity."

What do you know, Governor Dahlgren, about Scharnhorst's personal guard, her chosen elite?

Let me tell you what I have learned.

In attempts to raise support for the resistance I have paid visits to certain tribesmen I thought remained in sympathy with the Doctrine.

Sometimes I win a new supporter, sometimes I make a mistake.

Meanwhile, Hannah, you will go to Jack Tenrec, who, due to his own demons as well as our machinations, remains virtually sleepless.

As such, he is now in a very vulnerable, highly suggestible state of mind.
He should be overjoyed to again see the one person he trusts.

You will ask him to come with you to see Lord Drumheller who, you will explain, wishes to extend to him an official Wassoon welcome, clemency, and protection.

You will return his sidearm to him... loaded with our dummy bullets.

You will then lead Jack, and his carefully instructed guard, to the Grand Hall of Ancestors.

At the same time, the delegation from the City in the Sea will be led into the opposite end of the Grand Hall, ostensibly on their way to receive Tenrec.

Then, as both groups round the central fires...

As they pass the court slithers...

They will meet.
A shot will be fired and a carefully choreographed chaos will ensue...

Grandma's Last Quilt

From the editors of Traditional Quiltworks magazine

Traditional and Original Appliqué Designs by

Blanche Burkett White

(1895-1978)

CHITRA PUBLICATIONS

Your Best Value in Quilting

website: www.QuiltTownUSA.com

Copyright ©2000 Chitra Publications

All Rights Reserved. Published in the United States of America.
Printed in China.

Chitra Publications
2 Public Avenue
Montrose, Pennsylvania 18801-1220

No part of this publication may be reproduced or transmitted in any form
or by any means, electronic or mechanical, including photocopy, recording,
or any information storage and retrieval system now known or to be invented,
without permission in writing from the publisher, except by a reviewer
who wishes to quote brief passages in connection with a review
written for inclusion in a magazine, newspaper, or broadcast.

First Printing: 2000

Library of Congress Cataloging-in-Publication Data

Grandma's last quilt / from the editors of Traditional Quiltworks magazine ; traditional
and original appliqué designs by Blanche Burkett White (1895-1978)
   p. cm.
  ISBN 1-885588-35-6 (pbk.)
   1. Appliqué--Patterns. 2. Quilting--Patterns. I. White, Blanche Burkett, 1895-1978. II.
Traditional quiltworks

TT779.G73 2001
746.46'041--dc21

                                                                      00-064465

Edited by: Debra Feece
Design and Illustrations: Diane M. Albeck-Grick
Cover Photography: Van Zandbergen Photography, Brackney, Pennsylvania

Our Mission Statement:

*We publish quality quilting magazines and books
that recognize, promote and inspire self-expression.
We are dedicated to serving our customers
with respect, kindness and efficiency.*

www.QuiltTownUSA.com